50
THINGS
TO COLOR

METRO BOOKS
New York

An Imprint of Sterling Publishing
1166 Avenue of the Americas
17th Floor
New York, NY 10036

Cover design by Shelley Baugh.

ISBN 978-1-4351-5864-1

For information about custom editions, special sales, and premium and corporate purchases, please contact
Sterling Special Sales at 800-805-5489 or specialsales@sterlingpublishing.com.

Manufactured in China.

10 9 8 7 6 5 4 3 2 1

www.sterlingpublishing.com

50 THINGS TO COLOR

50 Creative Projects to Unleash Your Coloring Skills

Susan Hogan Tice

METRO BOOKS
New York

Table of Contents

Tools and Materials

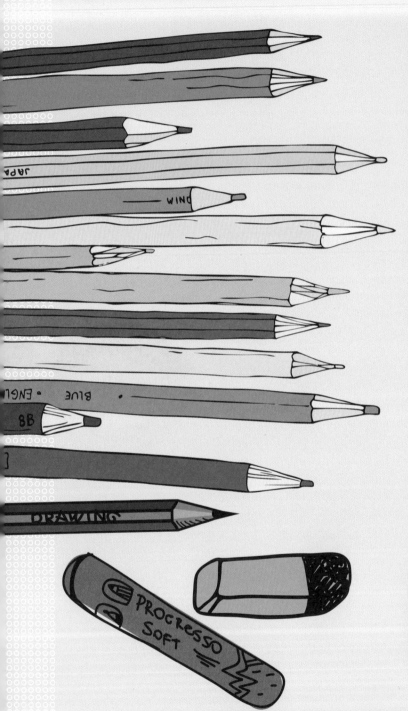

Colored Pencils

I recommend this starter set of colors: gray, mineral orange, espresso, crimson lake, indigo blue, magenta, true blue, dark green, light green, goldenrod, orange, poppy red, violet, and black. Many art and craft stores sell pencils individually, making it easy to mix and match your pencils and add to your color palette as needed.

Erasers

Use a rubber eraser to erase light applications of color when using colored pencils. You may also take a kneaded eraser and dab at the area to pick up the pigment. Wall mounting putty is very useful when used the same way. For stubborn areas, use a battery-powered eraser.

Sharpener

Use a hand-held sharpener to give your colored pencils sharp tips. A fine point can be used to create extremely thin lines and color in small details. You can also use the side of a sharp tip to produce thick strokes that are perfect for quickly coloring in large areas.

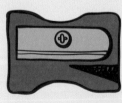

Paints and Paintbrushes

While you may not want to paint directly in the book, feel free to transfer these images to paper or canvas and bust out your acrylics, watercolors, or oils. The colors I recommend starting with are burnt sienna, crimson red, ivory black, lemon yellow, permanent green, ultramarine blue, and yellow ochre. You may also want to pick up Chinese white for lighter tints. You'll want a flat brush for covering large areas and applying washes, as well as a round brush with a tapered point for a variety of paint strokes and fine details.

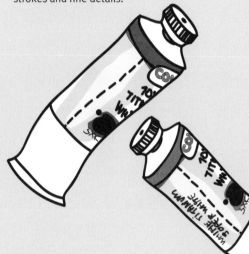

Markers

Whether permanent or magic, markers are a coloring must-have. The saturated hues of markers are bright and vibrant, just like the artist wielding them—you! Markers come in every color imaginable, and are readily available at all arts and crafts stores.

Crayons and Pastels

Instantly feel like a kid again opening an eight-pack, or go more advanced with a box of sixty-four or more. If crayons feel too childish to you, make them classy by going the pastel route. Pastels come in a variety of choices, mainly soft, hard, and oil, and can be used to create dazzling effects involving layered and mixed colors.

Warming Up

Just as you warm up before working out at the gym, you should relax your hand and get comfortable holding the utensils—be they crayons, markers, or in this case, colored pencils, before exercising your creativity. I usually warm up by drawing random squiggles and lines. Familiarize yourself with the different types of lines your pencils can create, and experiment with every kind of stroke you can think of, using both a sharp point and a blunt point. Practice the strokes below and on the next page to help you loosen up.

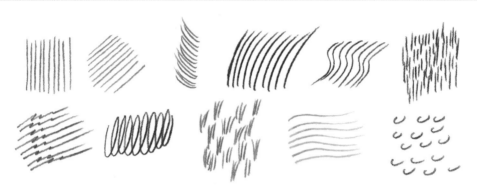

Coloring with a Sharp Point
First draw a series of parallel lines. Try them vertically; then angle them. Make some of them curved, trying both short and long strokes. Then try some wavy lines at an angle and some with short, vertical strokes. Try making a spiral and then grouping short, curved lines together. Then practice varying the weight of the line as you draw.

Coloring with a Blunt Point
Now try the same lines with a blunt point. Even if you use the same hand positions and strokes, the results will be different when you switch pencils. In the example above, you can see that the blunt pencil produced different images. You can create a blunt point by rubbing the tip of the pencil on a sandpaper block or on a rough piece of paper.

Starting Simply

First experiment with vertical, horizontal, and curved strokes. Keep the strokes close together and begin with heavy pressure. Then lighten the pressure with each stroke.

Varying the Pressure

Randomly cover the area with tone, varying the pressure at different points. Continue to keep your strokes loose.

Using Smaller Strokes

Make small circles for the first example. This looks like leathery animal skin. For the second example (at far right), use short, alternating strokes of heavy and light pressure to create a pattern that is similar to stone or brick.

Loosening Up

Use long vertical strokes, varying the pressure for each stroke until you start to see long grass (at near right). Then use somewhat looser movements that could be used for water (at far right). First create short spiral movements with your arm (above). Then use a wavy movement, varying the pressure (below).

Finding Your Style

After a while, you'll notice that your colorings will all take on a consistent look and feel. Don't worry — it's just your own unique style coming through. To jumpstart this process, try experimenting with the different types of linework shown below.

Using Criss-Crossed Strokes
If you like a good deal of fine detail in your work, you'll find that crosshatching allows you a lot of control. You can adjust the depth of your shading by changing the distance between your strokes.

Sketching Circular Scribbles
If you work with round, loose strokes like these, you are probably very experimental with your art. These looping lines suggest a free-form style that is more concerned with evoking a mood than with capturing precise details.

Making Small Dots
This technique is called "stippling" — many small dots are used to create a larger picture. Make the points different sizes to create various depths and shading effects. Stippling takes a great deal of precision and practice.

Simulating Brushstrokes
You can create the illusion of brushstrokes by using short, sweeping lines. This captures the feeling of painting but allows you the same control you would get from crosshatching. These strokes are ideal for a more stylistic approach.

Color Values

Value is the term used to describe the relative lightness or darkness of a color (or of black). By adding a range of values to your subjects, you create the illusion of depth and form. Value defines form, not color, so if you choose the appropriate values, the color isn't important—you can draw purple trees or blue dogs and still captivate your viewers.

Creating Form with Value In this example, you can see that the gray objects seem just as three-dimensional as the colored objects. This shows that value is more important than color when it comes to creating convincing, lifelike subjects. It's a good idea to practice this exercise before you begin the projects so you can get a handle on applying values. First view the basic shape. Then, starting on the shadowed side, begin building up value, leaving the paper white in the areas where the light hits the object directly. Continue adding values to create the form of the object. Squint your eyes to blur the details so you can focus on the value changes. Add the darkest values last. As the object gets farther away from the light, the values become darker, so place the darkest values on the side directly opposite the light.

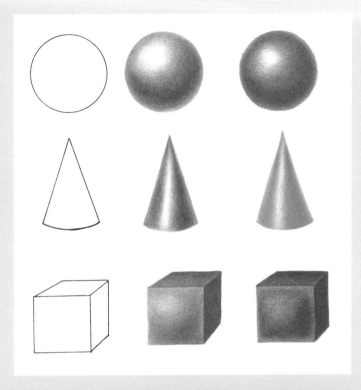

Value Scale Another helpful tool for understanding value is a value scale showing the progression from white (the lightest value) to black (the darkest value). Most colored pencil brands offer a variety of grays, which are distinguished by naming them either "warm" or "cool" and then adding a percentage to indicate the concentration of color, such as "cool gray 20%." (Lower percentages are lighter.) All different colors come in different values, too.

Light and Shadow

Shading gives depth and form to your coloring because it creates contrasts in *value* (the relative lightness or darkness of black or a color). In pencil drawing, values range from white (the lightest value) through different shades of gray to black (the darkest value; see the value scale below).

To make a two-dimensional object appear three-dimensional, pay attention to the values of the highlights and shadows. Imagine the egg below with no shading, only an outline. The egg would just be an oval. But by adding variations of value with light and shadow, the egg appears to have form. When shading a subject, you must always consider the light source, as this is what determines where your highlights and shadows will be. Keep in mind that shadows get darker as they get farther from the light source.

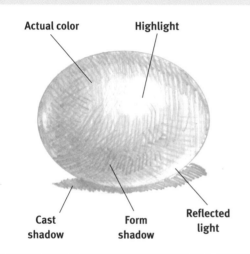

Actual color   Highlight

Cast shadow   Form shadow   Reflected light

Identifying Values

The *highlight* is the lightest value and is where the light source directly strikes the object. The gray area between the highlight and the shadow is the actual color of the egg, without any highlights or shadows. The *cast shadow* is the shadow that the egg casts onto the ground. The *form shadow* is the shadow that is on the object itself. *Reflected light* bounces up onto the object from the ground surface. (Most people don't notice that one!)

Value Scale

Making your own value scale will help familiarize you with the variations in value you can produce with a pencil. The scale also serves as a guide for transitioning from lighter to darker shades. Work from light to dark, adding more and more tone for successively darker values.

Basic Techniques

Below are examples of some of the most basic coloring techniques that you can use to replicate everything from smooth hair to rough wood. As you get your skills into shape, you can experiment and try new techniques. Whatever techniques you use, though, remember to shade evenly. Shading in a mechanical, side-to-side direction, with each stroke ending below the last, can create unwanted bands of tone throughout the shaded area. Instead, try shading evenly, in a back-and-forth motion over the same area, varying the spot where the pencil (marker, crayon) point changes direction.

Hatching
For this basic shading method, fill an area with a series of parallel strokes. The closer the strokes, the darker the tone will be.

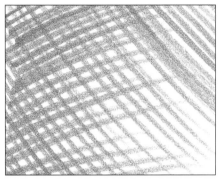

Crosshatching
For darker shading, place layers of parallel strokes on top of one another at varying angles.

Shading Darkly
Apply heavy pressure to the pencil to create dark, linear areas of shading.

Gradating
Apply heavy pressure with the side of your pencil, gradually lightening as you go.

Color Basics

Knowing a little about basic color theory can help you tremendously in drawing with colored pencils. The *primary colors* (red, yellow, and blue) are the three basic colors that can't be created by mixing other colors; all other colors are derived from these three. *Secondary colors* (orange, green, and purple) are each a combination of two primaries, and *tertiary colors* (red-orange, red-purple, yellow-orange, yellow-green, blue-green, and blue-purple) are a combination of a primary color and a secondary color.

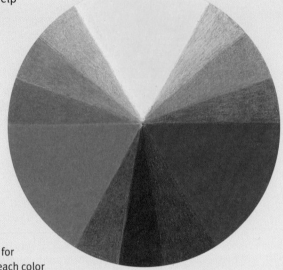

Color Wheel A color wheel is a useful reference tool for understanding color relationships. Knowing where each color lies on the color wheel makes it easy to understand how colors relate to and react with one another.

Complementary Colors

Complementary colors are any two colors directly across from each other on the color wheel (such as red and green, orange and blue, or yellow and purple). You can actually see combinations of complementary colors in nature—for instance, if you look at white clouds in a blue sky, you'll notice a hint of orange in the clouds.

Using Complements When placed next to each other, complementary colors create lively, exciting contrasts. Using a complementary color in the background will cause your subject to seem to "pop" off the paper. For example, you could place bright orange poppies against a blue sky or draw red berries amid green leaves.

Color Psychology

Colors are often referred to in terms of "temperature," but that doesn't mean actual heat. An easy way to understand color temperature is to think of the color wheel as divided into two halves: The colors on the red side are warm, and the colors on the blue side are cool. So colors with red or yellow in them appear warmer, and colors with more green or blue in them appear cooler. For instance, if a normally cool color (like green) has more yellow added to it, it will appear warmer; and if a warm color (like red) has a little more blue, it will seem cooler. Another important point to remember about color temperature is that warm colors appear to come forward and cool colors appear to recede; this knowledge is valuable when creating the illusion of depth in a scene.

Warm Versus Cool Here the same scene is drawn with two different palettes: one warm (below) and one cool (top). Notice that the mood is strikingly different in each scene. This is because color arouses certain feelings; for example, warm colors generally convey energy and excitement, whereas cooler colors usually indicate peace and calm.

Color Mood The examples here further illustrate how color can be used to create mood (left to right): Comp- lements can create a sense of tension; cool hues can evoke a

sense of mystery; light, cool colors can provide a feeling of tranquility; and warm colors can create a sense of danger.

Tints, Shades, and Tones

Colors can be tinted with white to make them lighter, shaded with black to make them darker, or toned with gray to make them more muted. Here each color was applied using graduated pressure—light, then heavy, then light. Black was applied at the top and white at the bottom to tint and tone the colors, respectively. To tint a color without muting it, apply the white first and then the color.

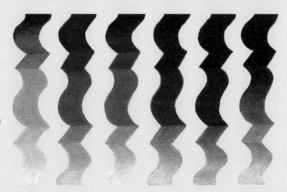

CHAPTER 1

Animals and Nature

Everyone's buzzing about this section—it's the bee's knees.

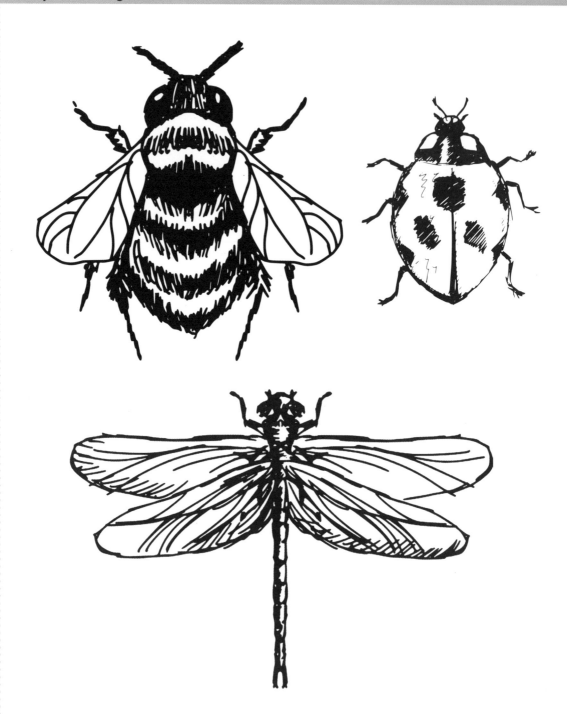

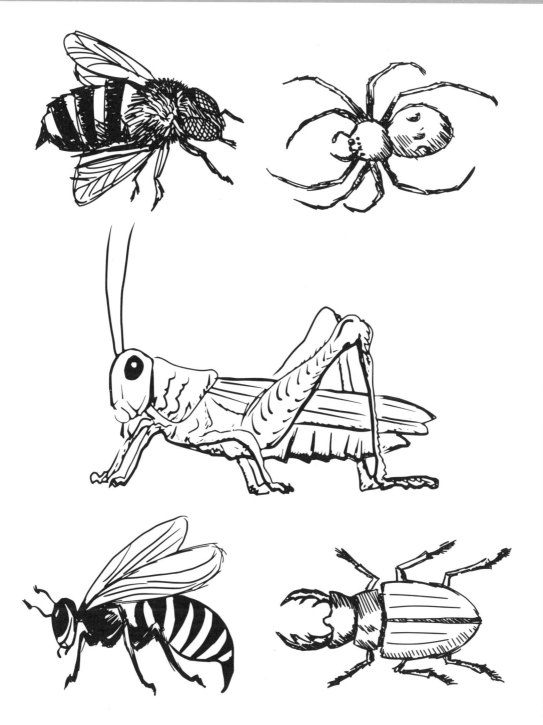

Dive into color with these underwater creatures.

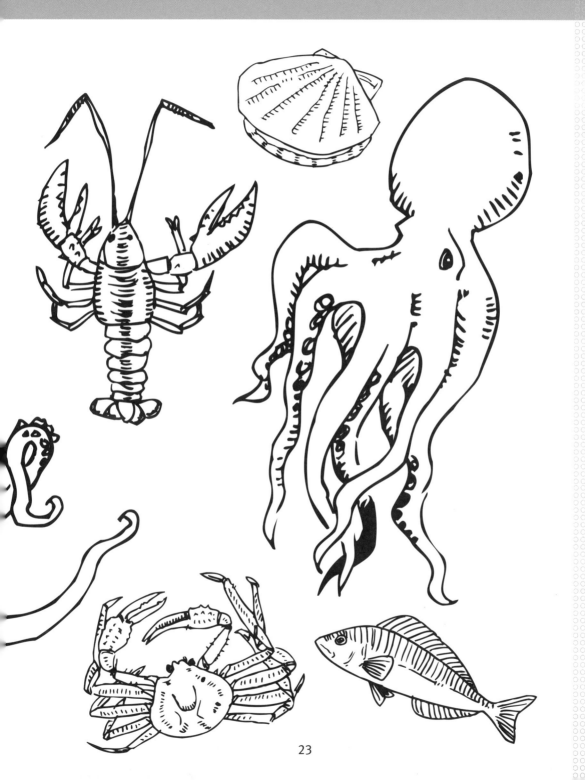

Little Red Riding Hood might have encountered creatures like these—beware of the big bad wolf!

Into the Wild

Roar and explore the habitat of these wild animals.

5 Birds

Birds of a feather flock to color.

Cats and dogs do get along—when you color them together.

Once you've leafed through this book, why not come back and color these trees?

Even in the desert, succulents bring a pop of color.

9 Flowers

Ever been told not to pick the flowers? Pick one here—or pick all of them—to color.

Flutter along with these fantastic creatures.

String theory holding the universe together? I think we're unified by color.

People and Fashion

Pack up, and let's get ready for the next adventure.

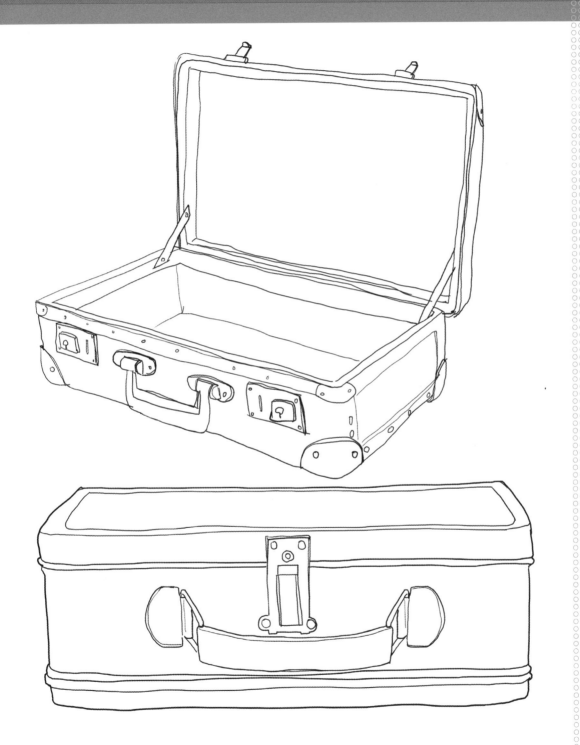

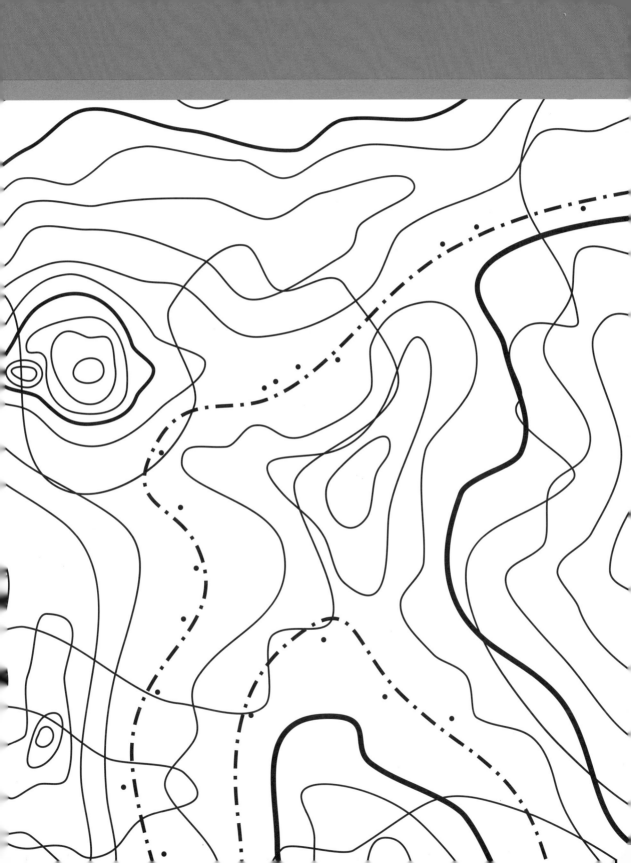

You know what they say: When the shoe fits... color it!

15 Hats

From bonnet to fedora, nothing tops a good hat!

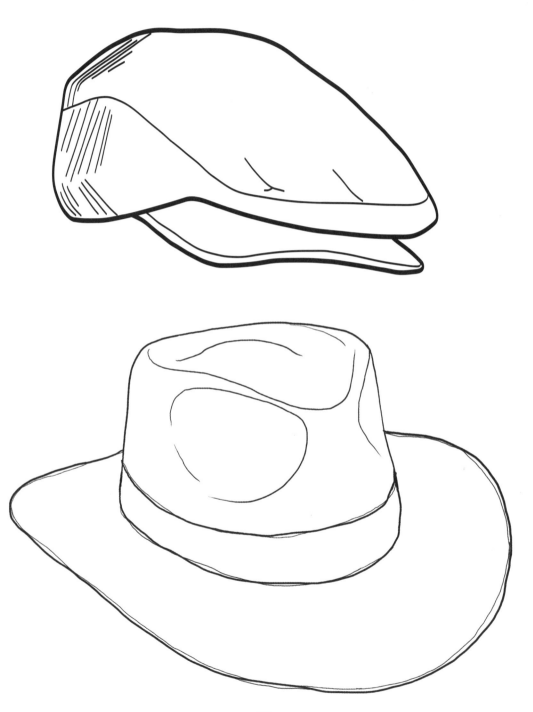

Color
this
Pattern

Splish splash! Bundle up and grab your umbrella—we're in for rainy weather!

Color
this
Pattern

Definitely not just a black tie event.

Color
this
Pattern

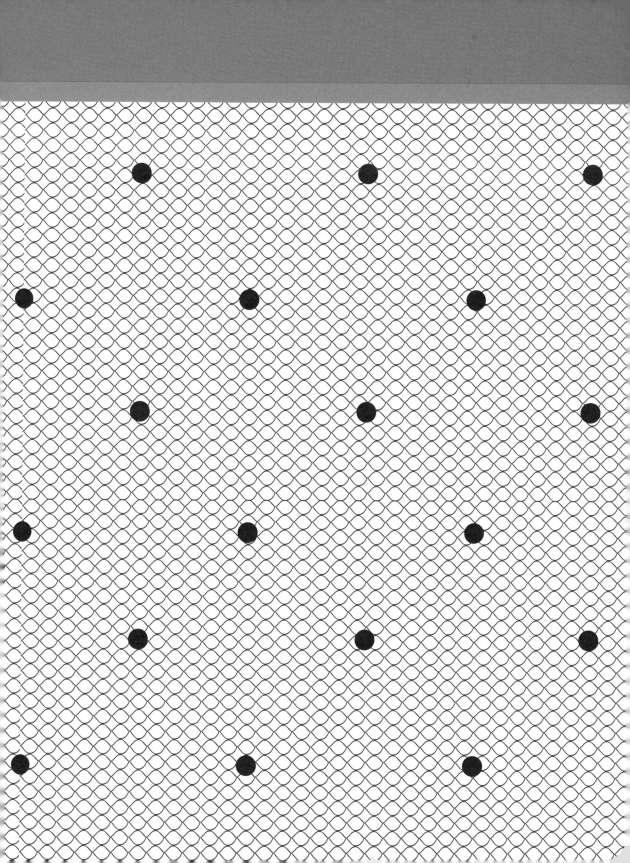

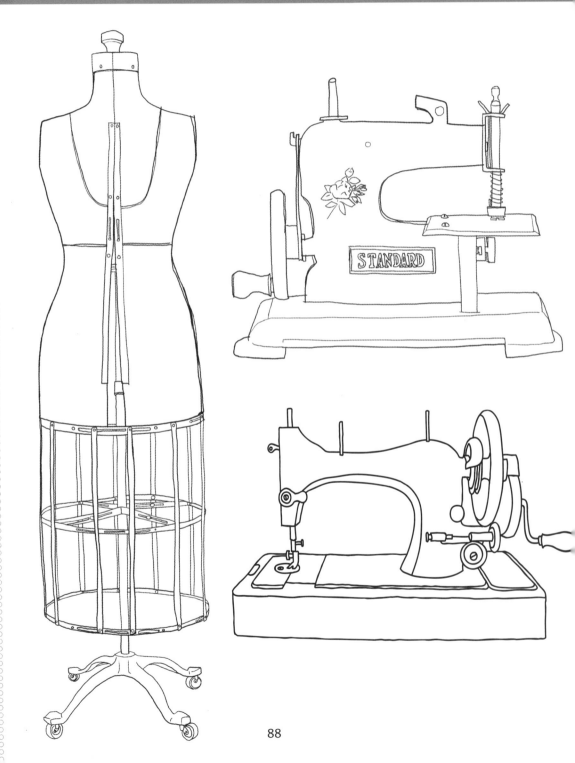

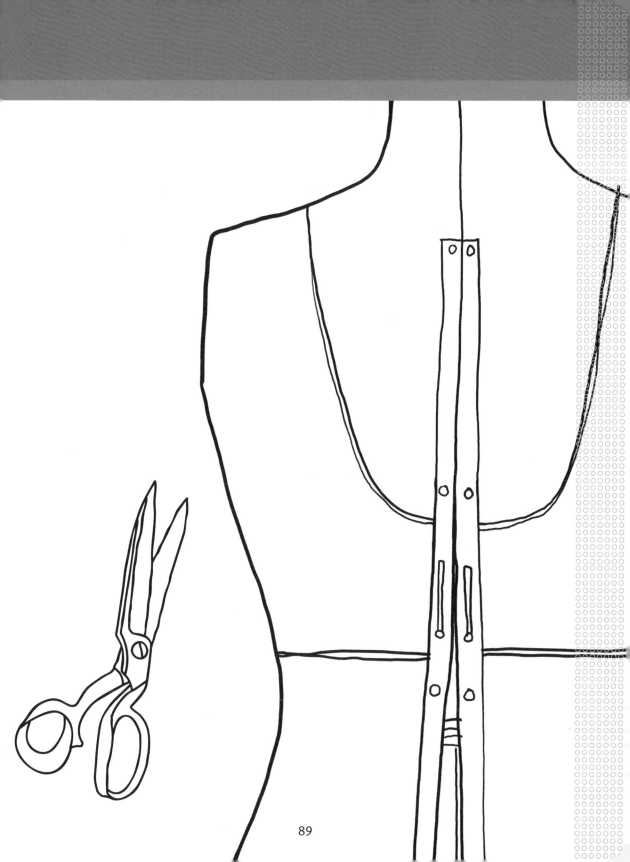

CHAPTER 3

Food and Drink

Not just good for you, they're also artistically interesting.

Have a seat at the sushi bar and relax.

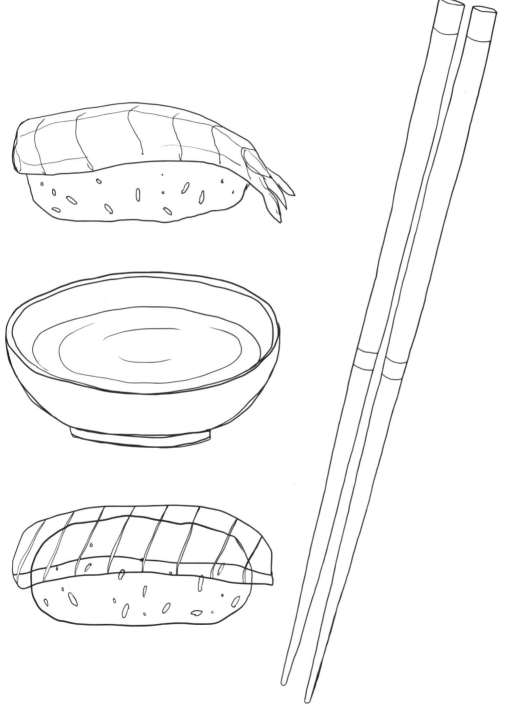

Perk up with a colorful cup o' joe!

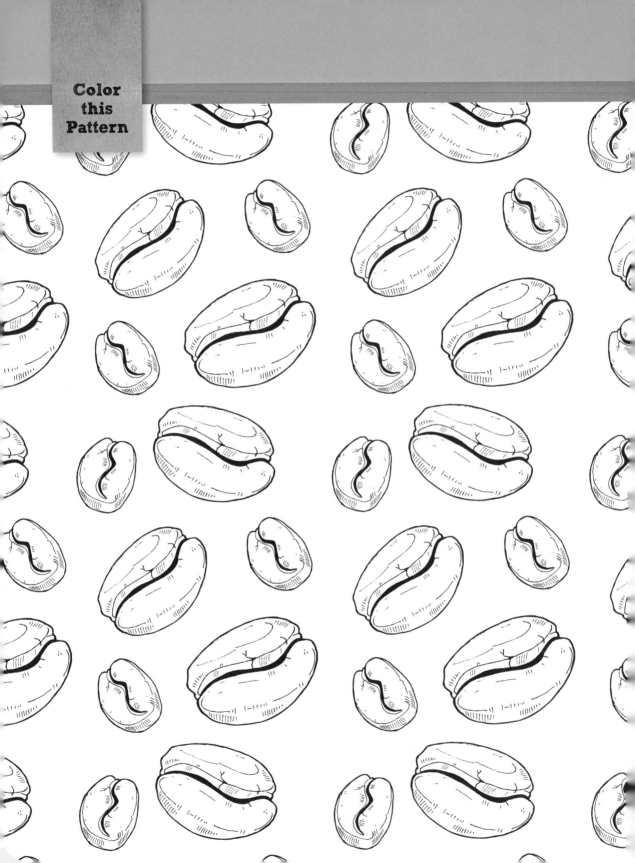

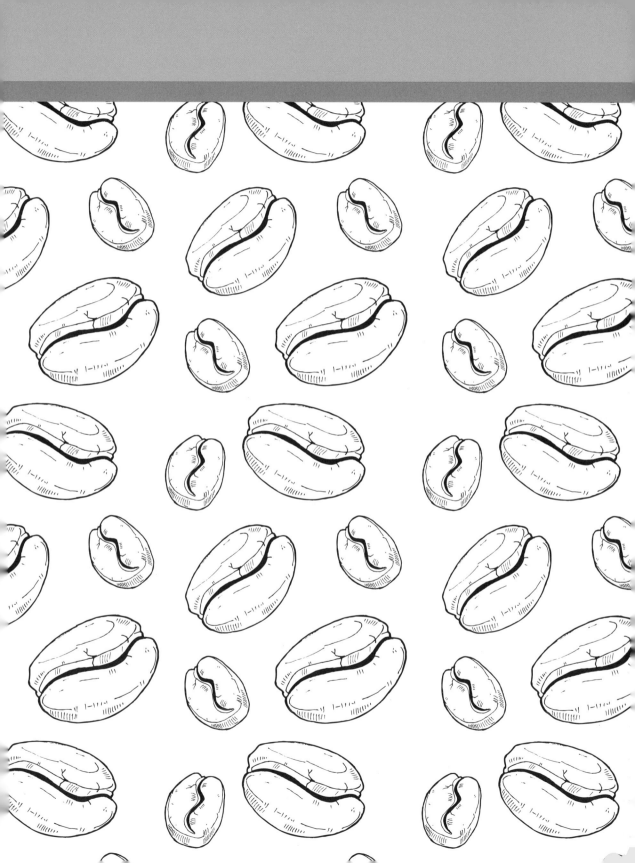

Scoop me up a double fudge banana split with extra colorful sprinkles.

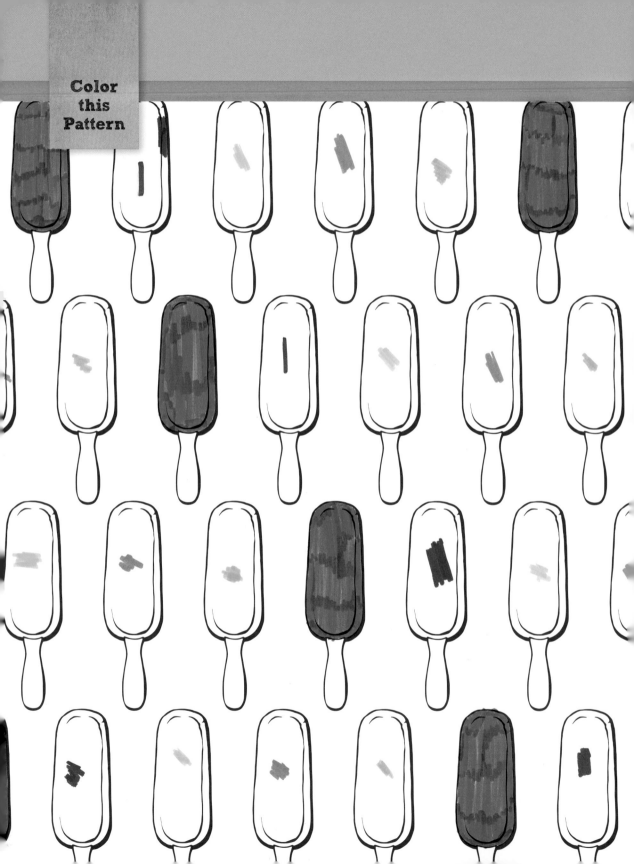

Color
this
Pattern

Oodles of hued noodles.

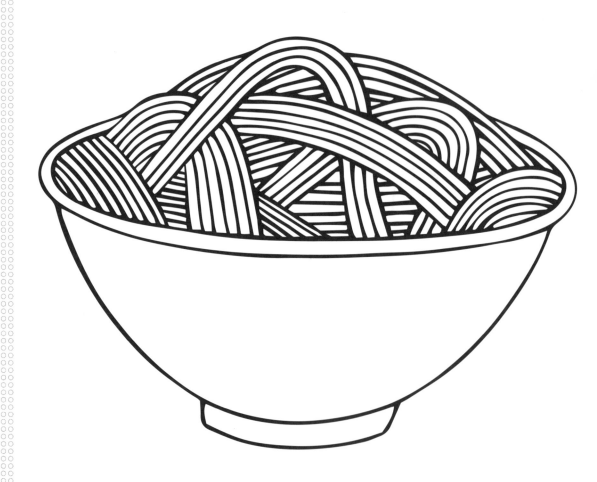

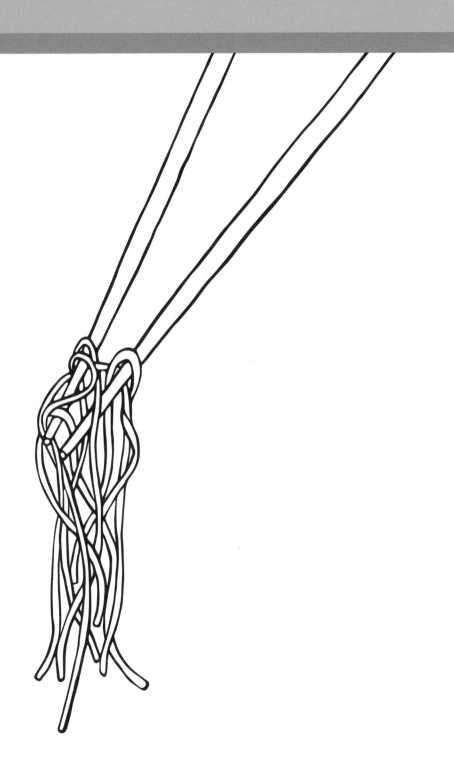

26 Cupcakes

Guilt free! Enjoy all seven cupcakes—with no worries of calories.

I'm sweet on color!

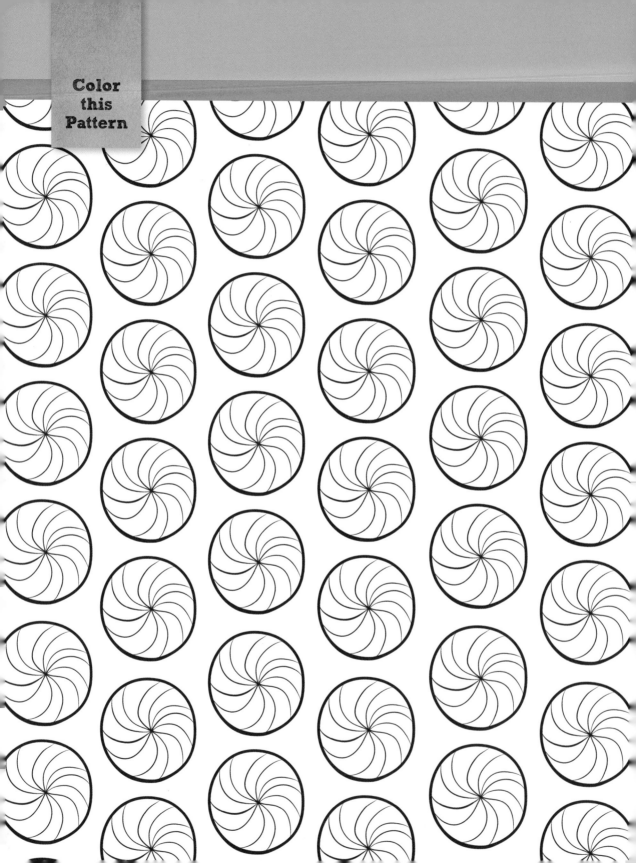

Mouthwatering donuts...now all I need is a cup of coffee for dunking.

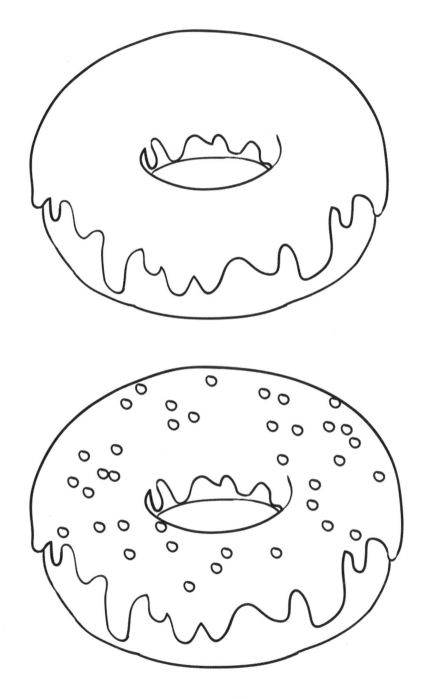

Color
this
Pattern

CHAPTER 4

Still Lifes and Other Objects

Tick. Tock. Color a clock.

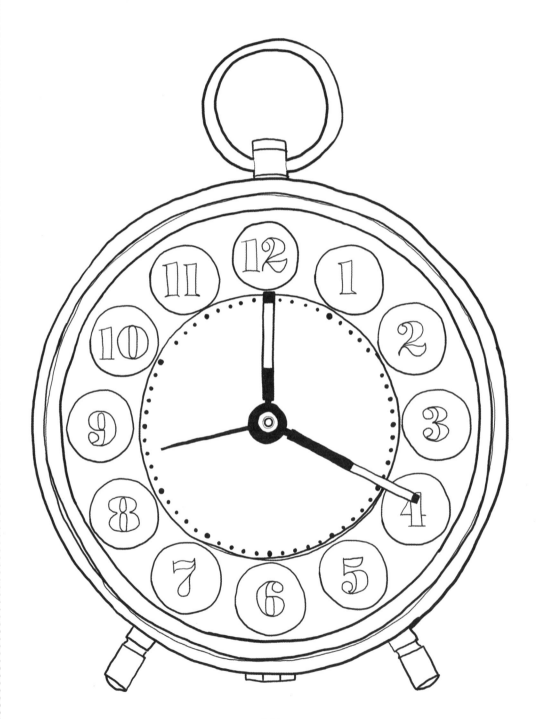

Ding! That's the sound to quit clacking on the keys—and get coloring these.

Color this Pattern

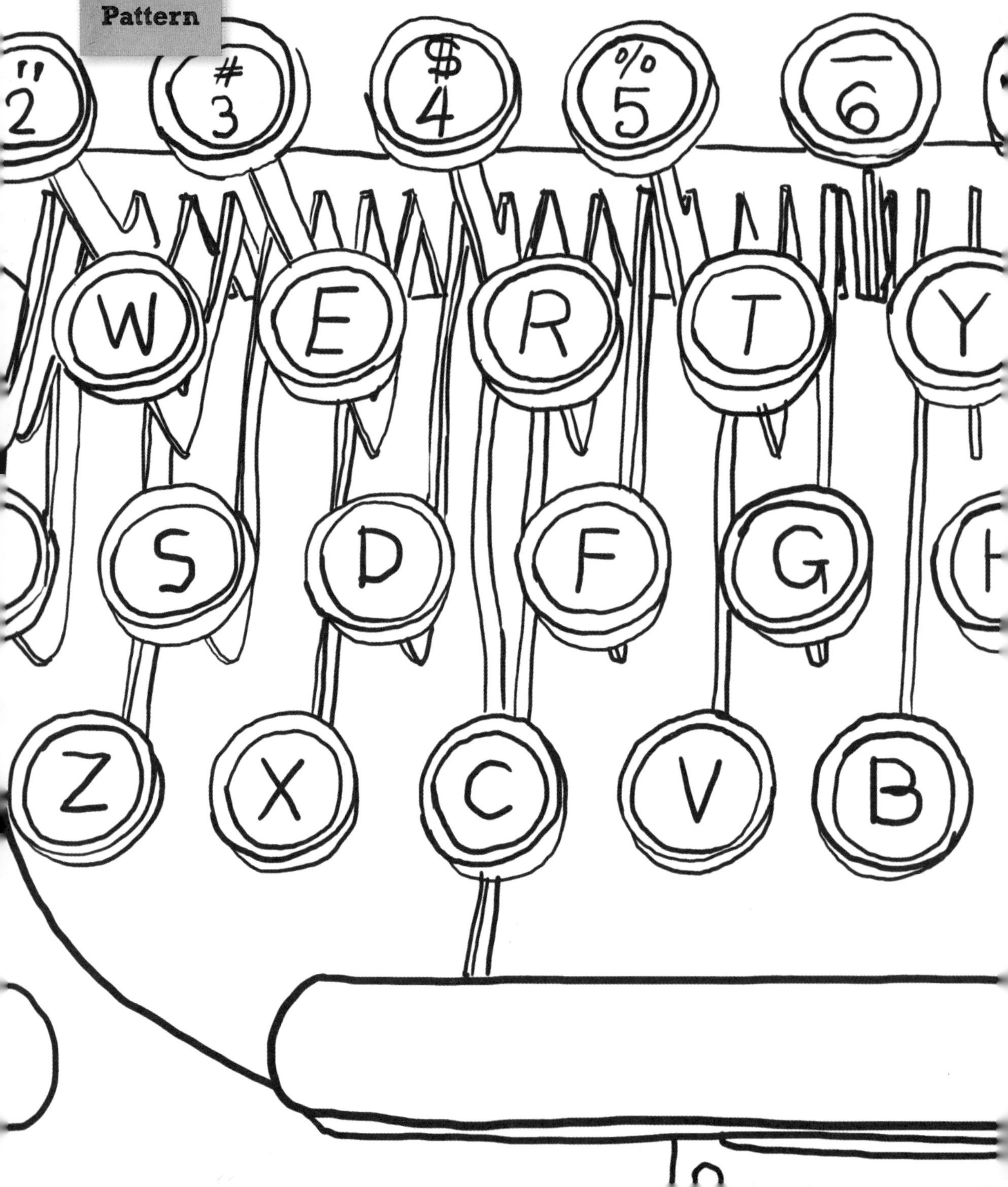

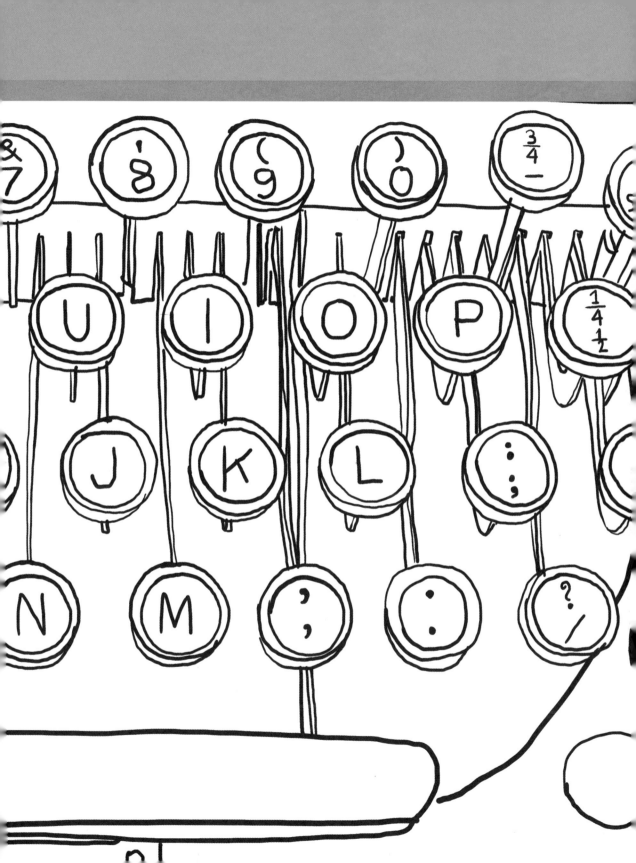

Groove on the sounds of yesterday, today.

160

Color
this
Pattern

37 Cameras

The focus here is color.

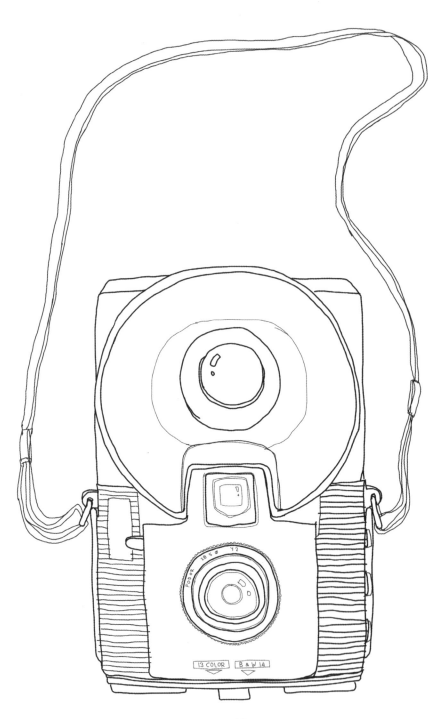

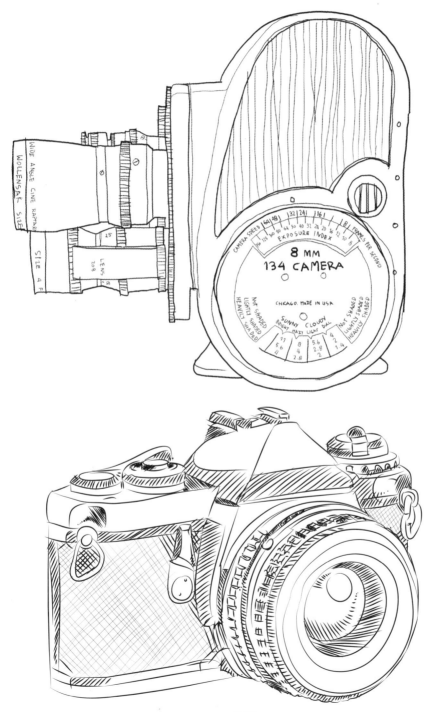

Tune that dial and find the perfect station for coloring elation.

It's a formal dinner party, and every color's invited.

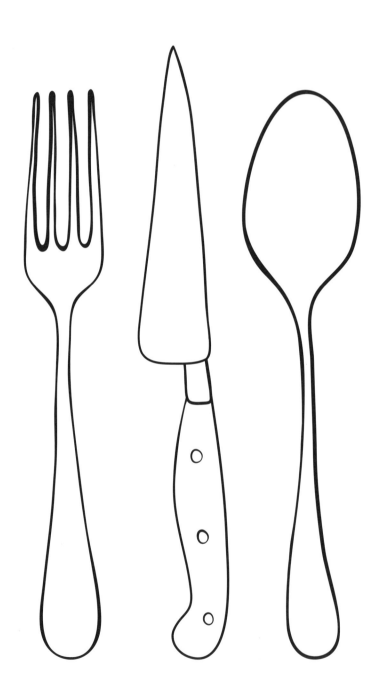

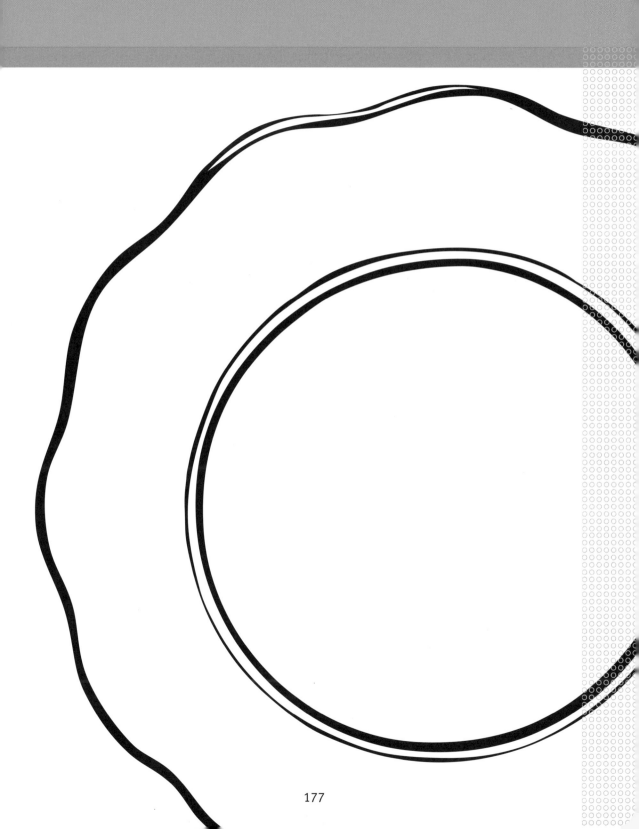

Color
this
Pattern

It's not a virtual wasteland if you're coloring TV's...

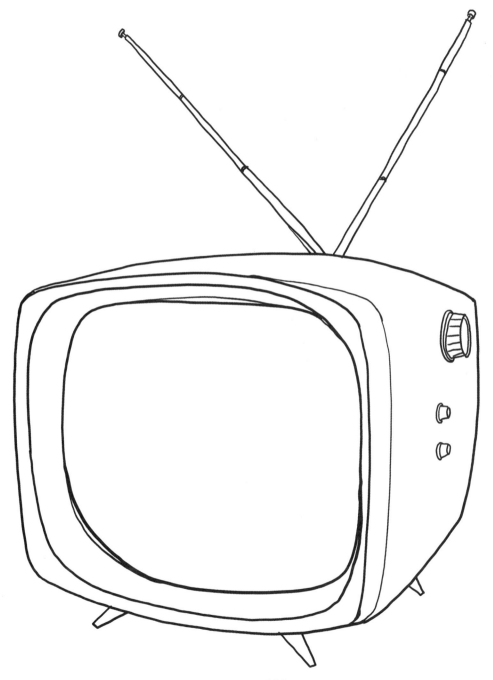

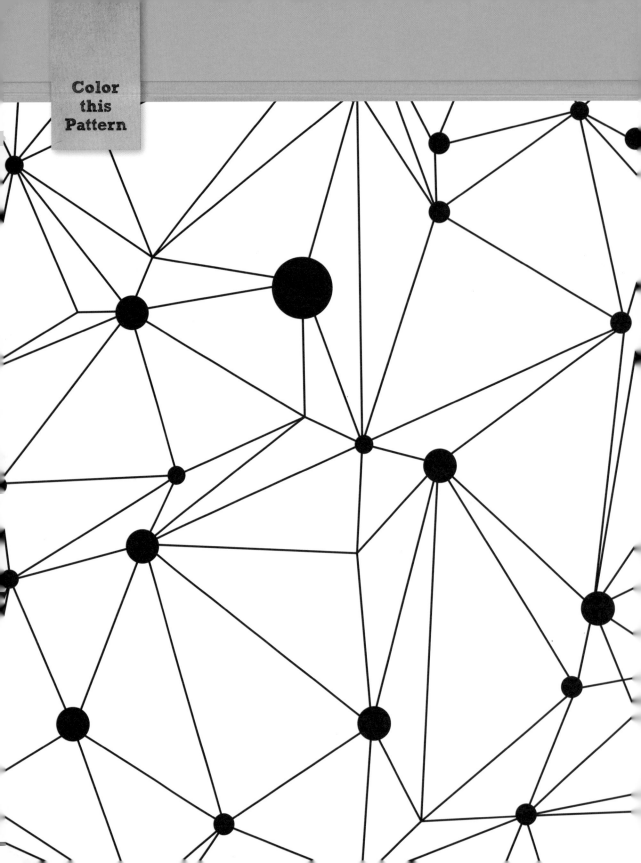

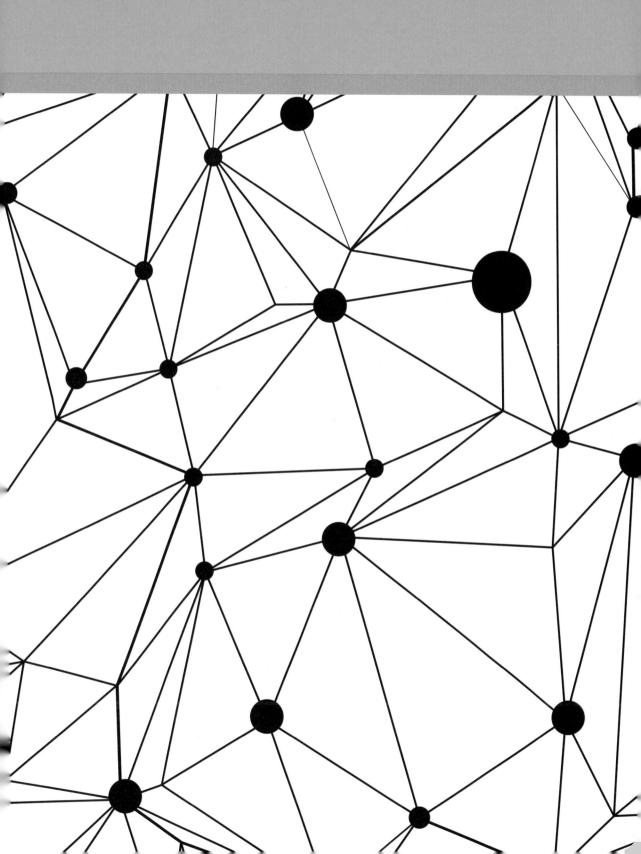

41 Musical Instruments

Our color goes up to 11.

Quaint and quirky.

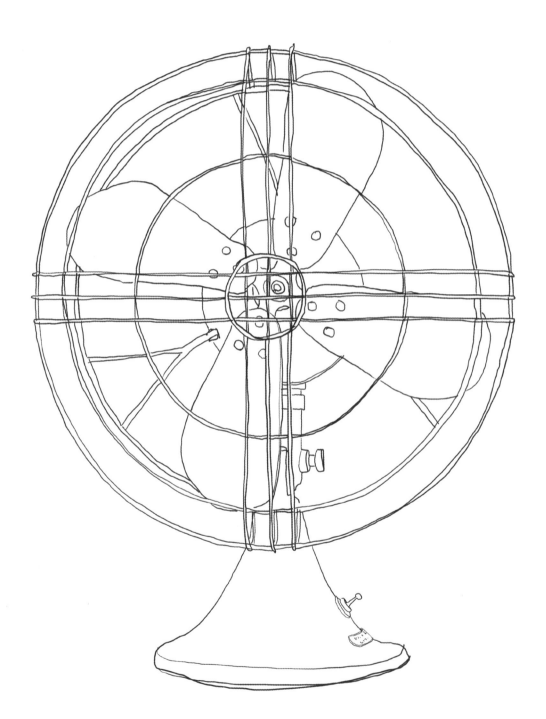

Color
this
Pattern

Ring! Ring! It's color calling.

46 Buildings

I can see my house from here! (It's the neon one.)

Color
this
Pattern

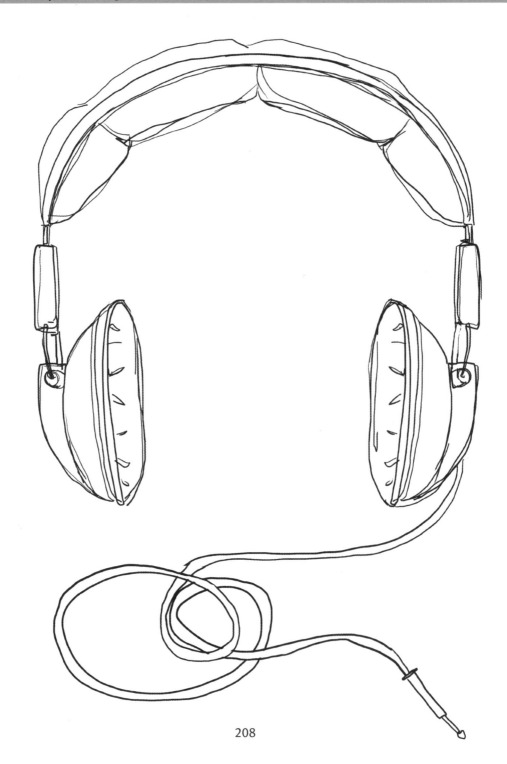

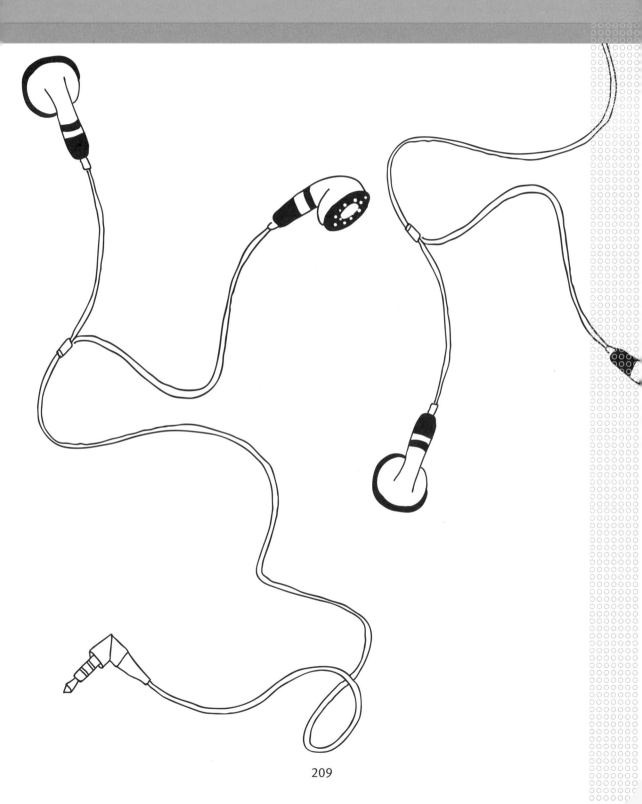

Color this Pattern

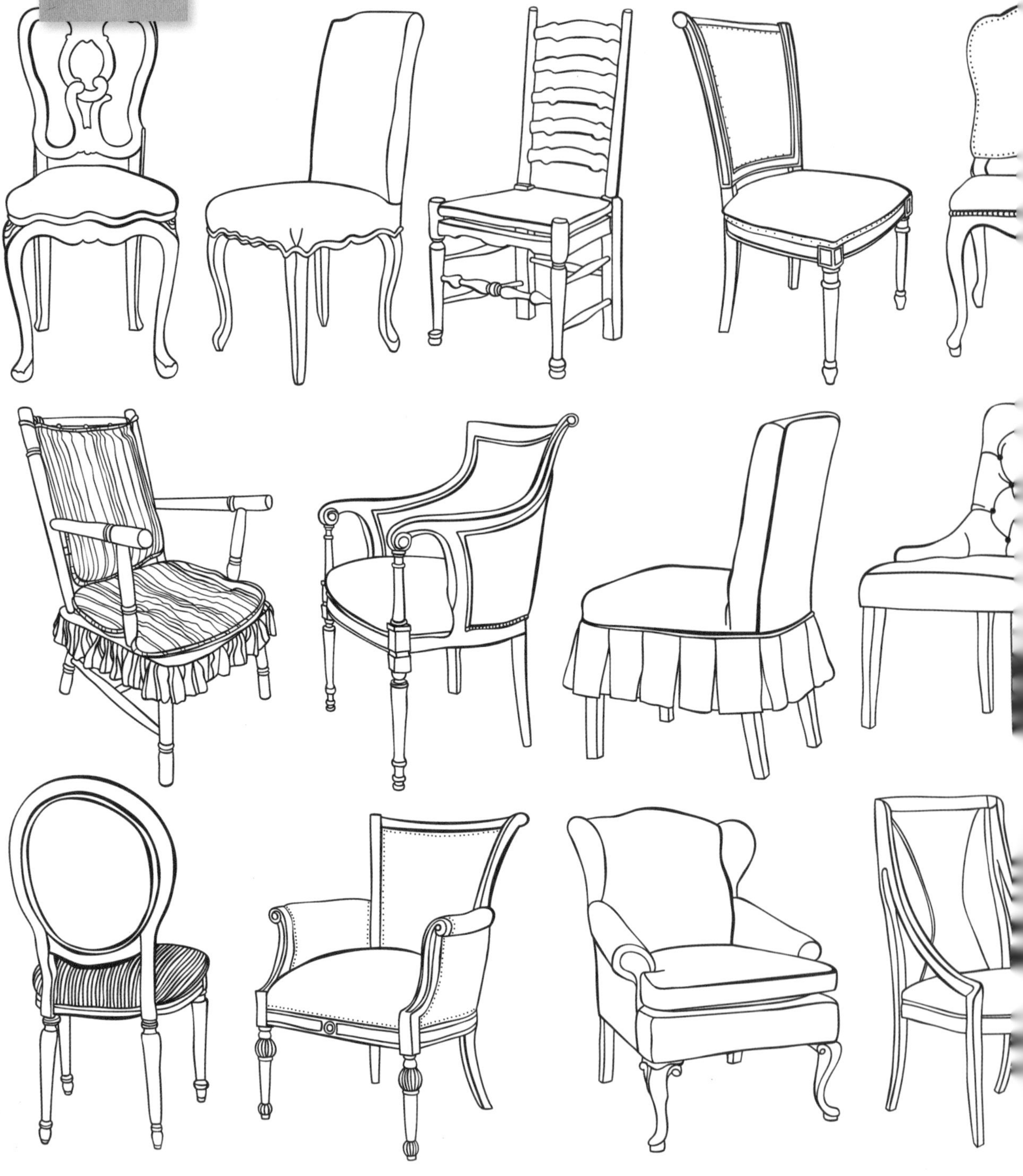

The key to relaxation? Open the door to color.

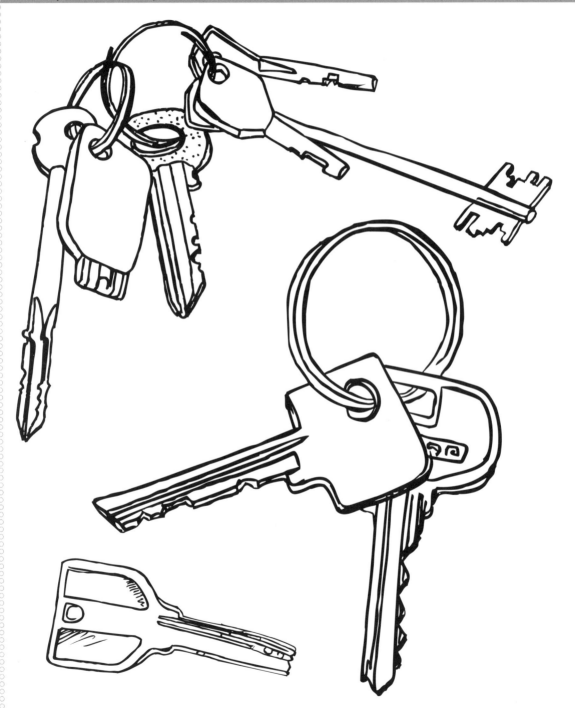

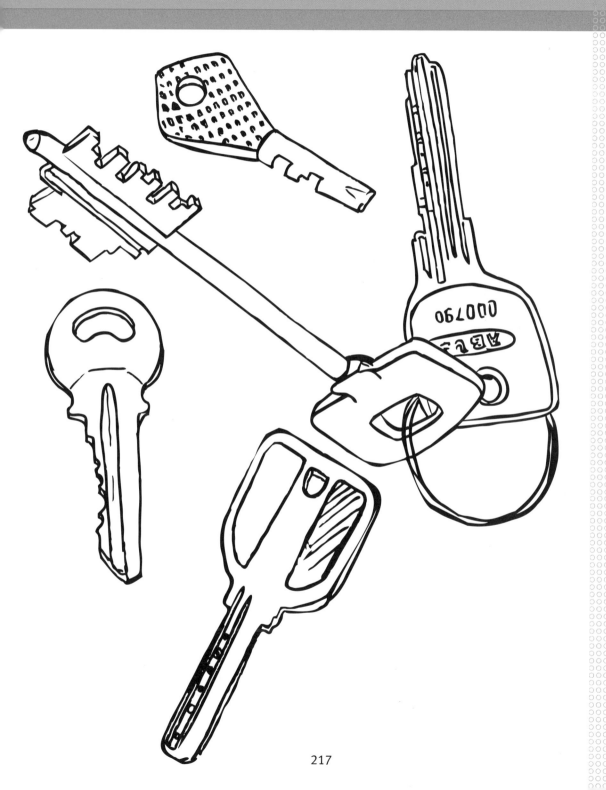

Day-glo school bus? What about a double-decker!

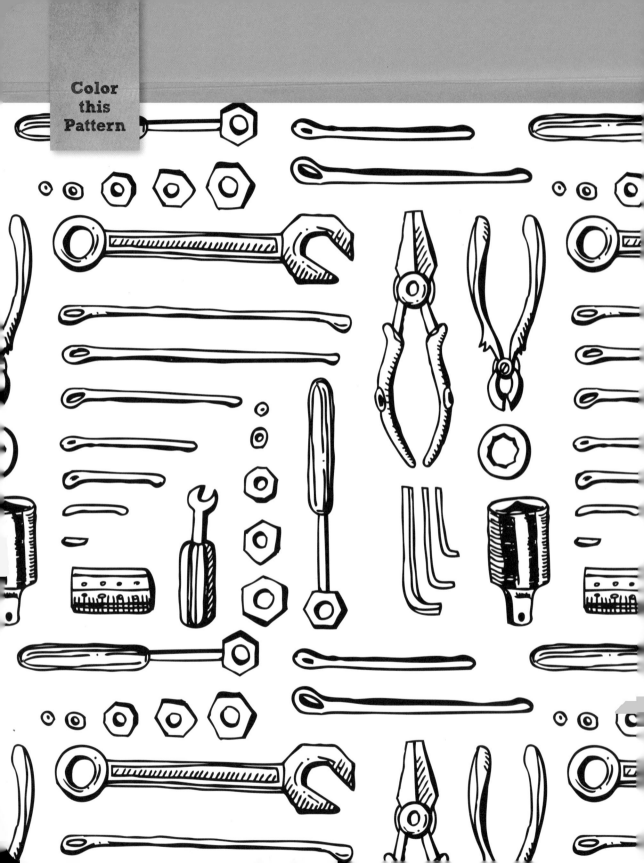

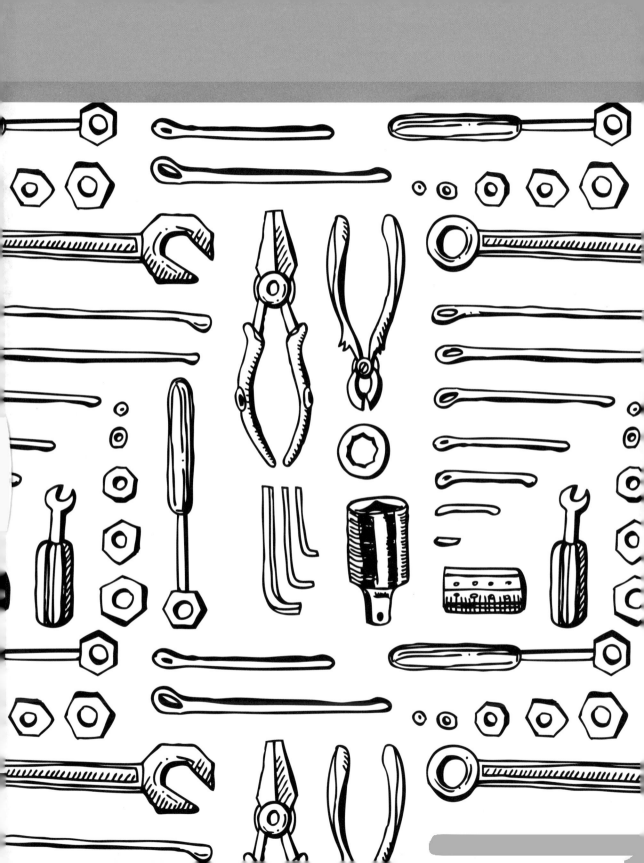

Infinite Things to Color

You've just been initiated into a world of color—a world where hues of vibrancy glow in places you would never expect—the side of a double-decker bus, a typewriter, sunglasses... and places you might, like a shiny scarab beetle, robust autumn leaves, and packed suitcases, but perhaps in colors not necessarily expected. (Neon trees? Why not?) There might be fifty things to color here, but there's countless more beyond. You're armed with inspiration. Color your world bold and bright.